Out came the **sunshine** and dried up all the rain,
So Incy **Wincy** Spider climbed the **spout** again.

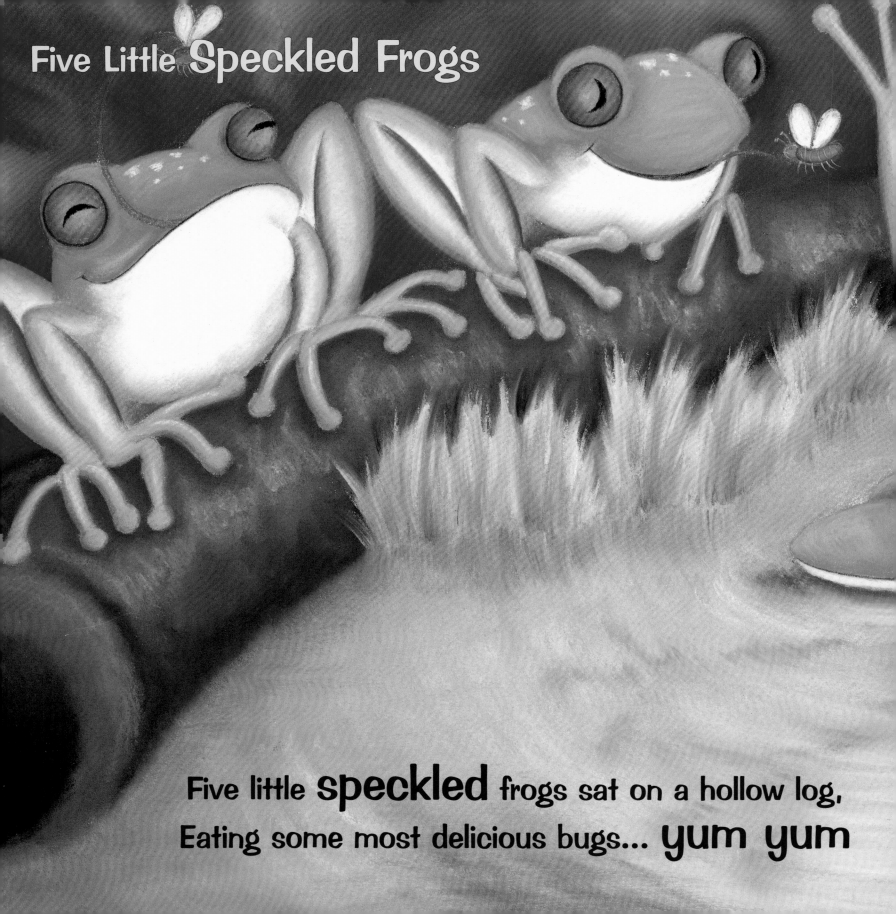

Five Little Speckled Frogs

Five little **speckled** frogs sat on a hollow log,
Eating some most delicious bugs... **yum yum**

One **jumped**
into the pool
where it was
nice and cool.
Then there were four
green speckled frogs
... **glub glub.**

continue counting backwards as follows

Four little speckled frogs ...

Three little speckled frogs ...

Two little speckled frogs ...

One little speckled frog ...

And now there are no green speckled frogs... glub glub.

One, Two, Three Four Five

One... **two**... three, four, five,
Once I caught a fish alive.
Six... seven... eight, **nine**, ten
Then I let him go again.

Why did you let him go?
Because he bit my **finger** so.
Which finger did he bite?
This **little** finger on my right.

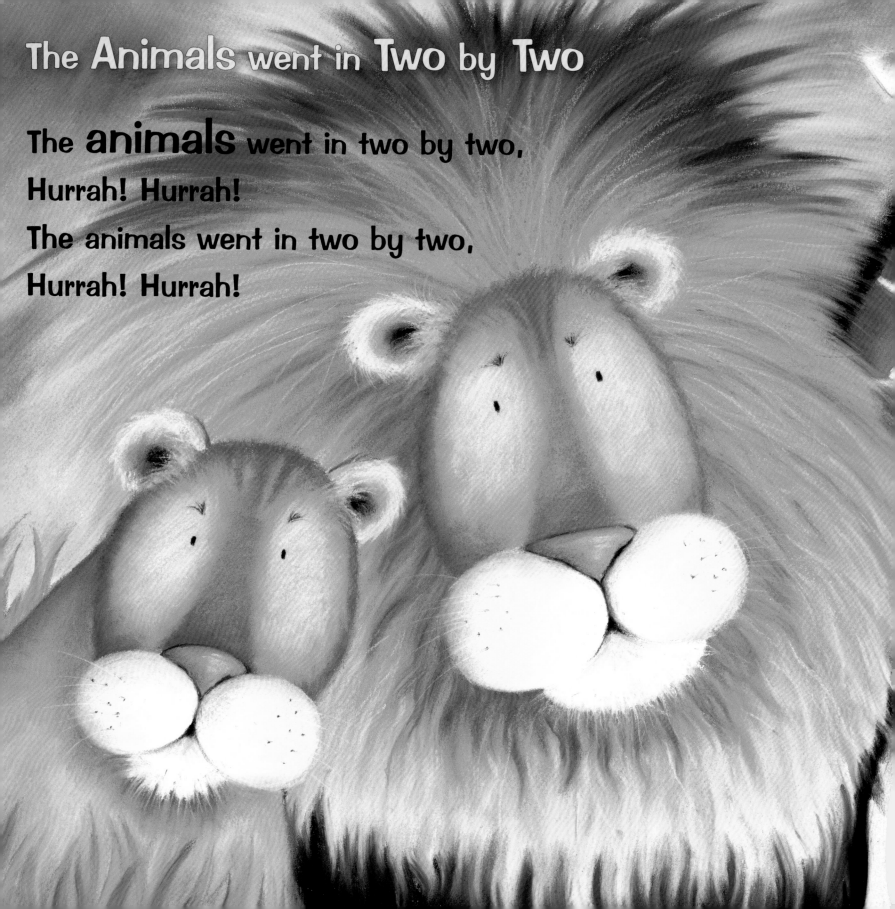

The Animals went in Two by Two

The **animals** went in two by two,
Hurrah! Hurrah!
The animals went in two by two,
Hurrah! Hurrah!

The animals went in two by two,
Giraffes and **lions** and zebras, too,
And they all went in
For to get out of the rain.

Row, Row, Row your Boat

Row, row, row your boat,
Gently down the stream.
Merrily, merrily, merrily, merrily,
Life is but a dream.